Ollie
&
Matilda

We all have a Special Gift
Within us, you Just need to
believe in yourself to release it.

So believe and your dreams
Come true!.

Love Christie
xx

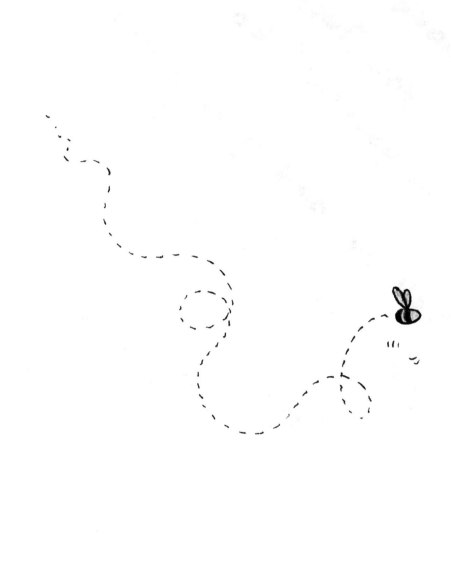

# This book
## belongs to

........................................

........................................

Acknowledgements

This book is dedicated to all of the amazing family and friends who inspired me to pursue my dream, you will never know how much you have helped me and I really do thank you all from the bottom of my heart. There are too many to mention you all by name but I would like to specifically thank Alison, Jenn and Becky for all your help and support.

Special thanks go to my darling husband Dean for believing in me and being there to keep me going even when at times I wasn't sure if I could continue and to my two sons Sean and Joshua for being the inspiration for all my future dreams.

Frickel
and the
Golden
Locket

Written by Christine Fox
Illustrated by Jenn Garside

This is Mia
and her new home,
where she has a
room of her own.

A room with a window
where Mia can see
the secret garden
beyond the big tree.

A secret garden
where Mia had found
a very tall flower
growing out of the ground.

A special sunflower
with a very long stalk
that to her surprise
could smile and talk.

"You look sad,"
the sunflower said.
Mia stepped back
and shook her head.

"I can't read as
well as my friends.
Can you help me?"
"That depends!"

"If you could have one
wish, what would it be?"
"To write a book
for all to see."

"Then my friend Frickel
is the one you need.
He can help, and will
teach you to read."

Mia went back to the garden
the very next day,
excited to hear what
the sunflower would say.

Mia was surprised when she finally got there to see the sunflower and a frog smiling at her.

"Hello Mia," croaked
the frog out loud.
"My name is Frickel,"
he said as he bowed.

"I believe I am here
to help you," Frickel said.
"I hope so!" Mia replied
nodding her head.

Frickel smiled,
"I am sure I can.
If you have the desire,
then I have the plan."

He pulled from behind him
a very large book,
"Let's sit down together
and take a look."

Every day in the garden
you would see,
Frickel and Mia
sitting under the tree.

With help from Frickel,
Mia's reading got better,
she could understand words
and also the letters.

Now Mia wants to read
every single day,
with Frickel to show her
what the words say.

As the days went by,
Mia grew happier inside,
the more she read
the more she smiled.

The day had arrived
when Mia said, "Look!
There is only one page
left to read in this book."

"Yes," said Frickel,
"we are now at the end.
And now you can read
as well as your friends."

Mia couldn't help feeling
a little sad inside,
what would she do without
Frickel by her side?

"Don't worry," said Frickel, as he climbed onto the chair. "Whenever you need me, I will always be there."

Frickel reached deep into his pocket
and pulled out a beautiful golden locket.

Frickel crouched down
onto one knee,
"Look inside," he said,
and tell me what you can see?"

"It's just a mirror," said Mia,
"and I can see me."
"Exactly," said Frickel,
"and that's the key!

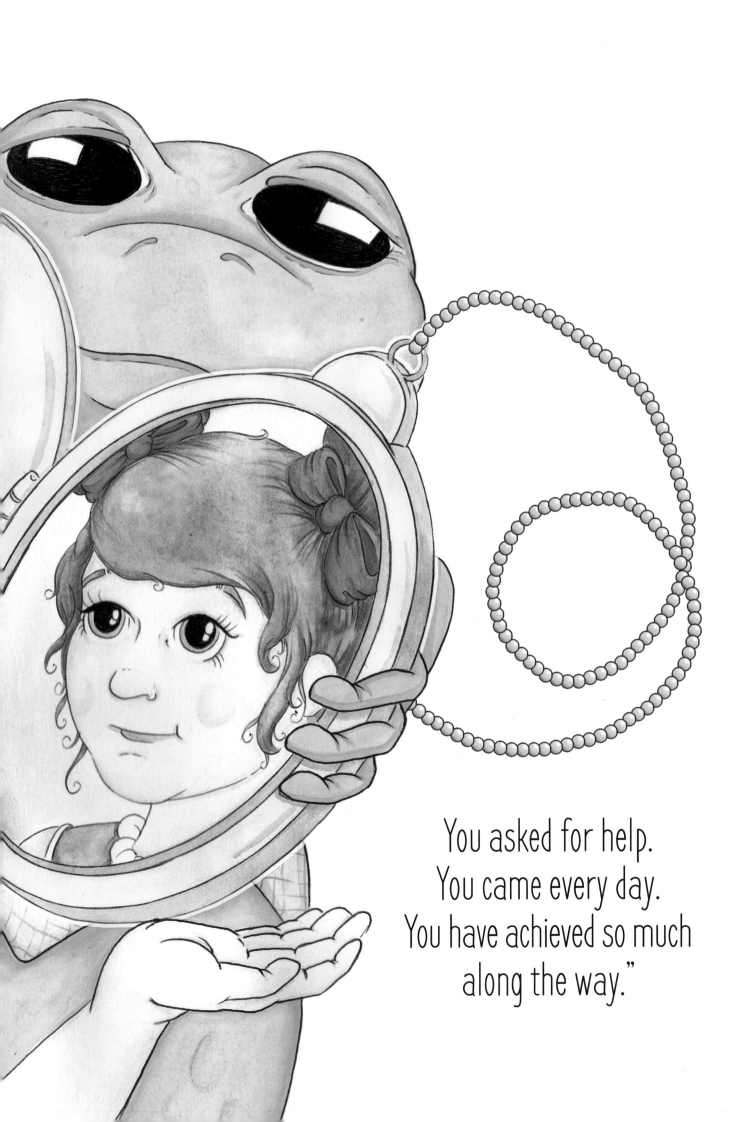

You asked for help.
You came every day.
You have achieved so much
along the way."

"You did the work," said Frickel,
"I was just the guide.
Everything you needed
came from inside.

It's my time to go now,
but even though we're apart,
I will always be with you
in your heart of hearts!"

"So the locket is my gift,
to help you to see,
that you can be
whatever you want to be!"

# My exciting picture

# I am so happy and excited

Photograph by:
Friend of the family, Matthew Nguyen

Hello, my name is Christine and I am a business owner, author, speaker and mum who grew up in the North East of England during the 1960's and 70's.

As a child I loved music, art and sport and dreamt of one day becoming a dancer, performing in front of thousands of people. However, I struggled during school with elements of reading and writing and was advised to go into something "more practical" as the academic requirements to get into a dance academy would be too difficult for me. This left me feeling insecure, vulnerable and lacking in self-belief.

So I left school and started an apprenticeship in hairdressing and I remained in that industry for most of my working life. At the age of 48 I was diagnosed with dyslexia, which helped explain some of the difficulties and frustrations I had felt at school.

Determined to succeed and make a difference, I have immersed myself in personal development to rebuild my self-confidence. I am now passionate about helping others who may be having similar experiences. In particular, I wanted to reach out to as many children as possible who might be feeling like I did.

I decided to write a book that would hopefully help inspire children who may be struggling with dyslexia, or feelings of insecurity and lack of self-belief. Empowering them to speak out, seek help and most importantly to believe in themselves and always follow their dreams.

If through this book I can have an impact on the life of even just one child, then I will have fulfilled my greatest ambition.

I want every child to know that they are special and they can "be whatever they want to be".

Published by: Sunflower Dreams Academy

ISBN 978-1- 5272-1172- 8

Illustrated by Jenn Garside

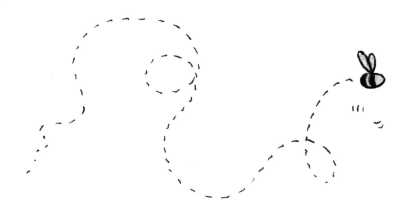